GRAYWINGS

GRAYWINGS

by Alice E. Goudey

Illustrated by Marie Nonnast

CHARLES SCRIBNER'S SONS · NEW YORK

GRAYWINGS

U. S1349035

This book is about Herring Gulls. There are many other kinds of gulls but the Herring Gulls are the ones we are most likely to see.

They live on both the East and the West Coasts and around lakes and rivers.

They are about two feet long. They have a wide wingspread between four and five feet. They weigh about two and one-half pounds.

Young Herring Gulls are speckled and dark in color. As they grow older they become lighter. When they are about four years old their heads and breasts become snowy white. Their wings and backs become a soft blue-gray color. When they are fully grown they have pink legs and a bright orange spot on the underside of their bills.

It is usually the young Herring Gulls that we see along the coasts in summer. Many of the older ones fly off to islands to build nests and raise their young. They do not come back to the mainland until late in summer.

All gulls have strong curved bills. Their three forward toes are connected by webs of tough, leathery skin which turn their feet into good paddles for swimming.

They will eat almost anything. For this reason they are very helpful in keeping the water clean in harbors around towns and cities. They also help keep beaches clean. The gulls that live around lakes and rivers eat many harmful insects.

The Ring-billed Gull is found on both coasts and around lakes and rivers. It is smaller than the Herring Gull and has a black ring on its bill. It has yellow-green legs.

The Great Black-backed Gull is larger than the Herring Gull. It is found in the Arctic and along the northeast coast. It has a black back and wings. This big gull is sometimes called "The Tyrant Gull."

The Laughing Gull is found on the Atlantic and Gulf coasts. It is the gull that cries "Ha-ha-ha-ah-ha-haah!" It is smaller than the Herring Gull. It has a darker back and wings. The hind edges of its wings are bordered with white. It has a black head in summer which turns lighter in winter.

The smallest American gull is called Bonaparte's Gull. It too is found on both coasts. It is a dainty little bird with a white triangle toward the end of its wings.

The little black-legged Kittiwake that calls "Keet! Keet!" is the most seagoing of all the gulls. It seldom comes close to shore unless driven in by a storm at sea. Its wing tips look as if they had been dipped in ink.

There are many other kinds of gulls but the ones mentioned above are the best known.

K ee-eer! Kee-eer! Kee-eer!"
scream the noisy herring gulls.
They fly high,
fly low,
rise again,
and circle and glide
like a whirling cloud
above the rocky little island.

Then, out over the sea,
and tilting their wings for a quick turn,
back again they swirl over the island.
"Kee-eer! Kee-eer! Kee-eer!"
It is the time of blue skies
and soft, warm winds.
It is the month of May,
and May is the time
when many gulls leave the mainland
and come to the little island
to build their nests.

Graywings drops down
and lights upon the ground.
"Klee-eew! Klee-eew! Klee-eew!"
she calls.
Big Graywings, her mate,
drops down silently
and stands beside her.
She pecks his bill lightly with her own
and makes soft sounds
to let him know
she likes him very much.
"Klee-eew! Klee-eew! Klee-eew!"
Big Graywings answers.
He speaks softly to his mate.

Beside a piece of driftwood
is a good place for a nest.
They scratch away the sand and pebbles
and make a little cup-shaped hole
in the earth.

They pull up grass by the roots
and carry seaweed from the shore
to line the little cup-shaped hole
they have made for their nest.

To the right,
to the left,
and all around the little island
other gulls have chosen places
to build their nests.
They are making cup-shaped holes,
pulling grass,
and carrying seaweed
from the shore.
Now, at last,
Graywings' nest is finished.

Settling down upon it,

she lays her first egg of the season.

Two days pass,

and then she lays another egg.

Two more days go by,

and then she lays her third egg.

"Klee-eew! Klee-eew! Klee-eew!"
Graywings murmurs softly
as she looks into the nest.
Oh, the wonder of the eggs—
olive-green splotched with black!

"Keeew! Keeew! Keeew!"
Big Graywings screams from his lookout
on the driftwood.
His screams say that there is danger.
A strange gull is too close.
The strange gull is a robber gull.

He swoops down to steal Graywings' eggs.
Big Graywings grabs the robber gull
by his bill.

He pulls the robber's wing.

Then Big Graywings flaps his wings
and, using them as clubs,
beats the robber gull.

At last, the robber runs off screaming.

Gently, carefully,
Graywings settles down upon her eggs.
The soft white feathers of her breast
keep them warm.

To the right,
to the left,
and all around the little island
other gulls sit upon their eggs
and keep them warm.

Sometimes storm clouds roll across the sky,
lightning flashes,
and rain pours down.
But the gulls stay quietly on their nests.

The father gulls take their turns
sitting upon the eggs.
Big Graywings takes his turn
while Graywings
soars above the island
or hunts for crabs and snails and little fish
along the water's edge.

Sometimes she rides upon the water,
rocking,
            rocking,
                        rocking
with the gentle movement of the waves.

And so four weeks of time pass by.
One day
Graywings hears a little tapping sound
beneath her breast.
A baby gull
inside an egg
is tapping against the shell.
He is tapping
with the sharp little egg tooth
on the top side of his bill.
Graywings listens.
Before long
she hears the shell
cracking, cracking, cracking.

And then,

there in a little opening in the shell

is a baby gull's

dark-colored bill.

The baby gull pushes hard

and breaks the shell wide open.

There he is—

a scrawny little thing,

all wet and panting from his struggle.

A tiny gull must be kept warm—
always warm.
Graywings gently covers the baby gull
with the soft feathers of her breast.
The next day
another baby gull breaks its shell.
And on the day that follows,
the third olive-green egg cracks wide open.
Graywings sits lightly on the nest
and spreads her wings above her babies.
Little gulls must stay safely
beneath their mother
until their downy coats are dry.

Before the sun goes down that day
Graywings rises from the nest.

Now the baby gulls are dry.

Now their downy coats are fluffy.

They look like little puff balls—

buff-gray specked with black.

"Peep! Peep! Peep!"

The little gulls call in squeaky voices.

Baby gulls are *always* hungry.

Big Graywings flies low across the water
bringing food.
Big Graywings lights beside them.
The babies spread their tiny wings,
and,
with open mouths,
beg for their first meal.
They peck at the bright orange spot
on Big Graywings' bill.

Big Graywings has brought fish,
carrying it home in his stomach.
Now he brings it up
to feed his hungry babies.

He holds small bits
in his strong curved bill
and lets them peck at it.

When the hot sun beats down
on the little island,
the baby gulls stand
in the shadows of their mothers
to keep cool.

When rain pours down,
they find shelter
under the spreading wings
of their mothers.

In a few days
little gulls
to the right,
to the left,
and all around
are running,
jumping,
flapping wings.
The little gulls were born to fly
but their tiny wings
are not yet strong enough
to carry them above the ground.

"Keeew! Keeew! Keeew!"
Graywings screams from the lookout
on the driftwood.
She is warning all the gulls
there is danger,

       danger,

            danger!

A big hawk is in the sky.
The little gulls run
to find
safe hiding places.

Some hide beside a big gray stone.

Some hide beside a piece of driftwood.

Some hide among the seaside grasses.

They crouch down flat against the sand.

Little gulls are so much the same color
as stone and driftwood,
sand and brown seagrasses
that the sharp-eyed hawk
does not see them hiding there.

The little herring gulls grow very fast
and change their downy coats
for feathers of dark gray
specked with brown.
To keep their feathers
smooth and shining
they preen them with their bills.

To clean their bills after eating
they poke them in the sand
and scratch them with a webbed foot.

Even though the little gulls
have grown quite large
they are still obedient
and walk quietly
behind their parents.

And then

one day they spread their wings

and leave the ground.

At first they flutter just above the rocky shore

and then drop down to rest.

But within a day or two

they soar above the island,

above the white-capped waves.

Hundreds of young gulls

hatched upon the rocky little island

are in the air!

Wheeling, circling, dipping,

they mingle with their parents

high above the land and sea.

Six weeks later
Graywings' children are full grown
and do not need her care.
Now she is free to fly off by herself,
to rock upon the waves
and hunt along the shore.
One day she finds a hard-shelled clam.

But even her big bill is not strong enough
to open it.
She picks it up and soars upward toward the
        sky.
When she has risen high above the shore
she lets it fall.
The hard-shelled clam goes tumbling down,
and when it strikes a rock
it breaks in little pieces.
Then Graywings swoops down
and eats the juicy clam
she finds inside the broken shell.
"Kee-eer! Kee-eer! Kee-eer!"
The other gulls hear Graywings screaming.

In the distance
there is a fishing boat at sea.
A fishing boat means food for gulls.
Graywings and a cloud of gulls
fly toward the boat.

The fishermen throw overboard
the fish too small to take to market.
Fluttering,
            squawking,
                        screaming,
                                    fighting,
the gulls swoop down
to eat the silvery fish.

A cold wind blowing from the north
tells the gulls that summer is over
and winter is on the way.
It is time to leave the little island
and fly back to the coast along the mainland
where there will be food for winter.
Graywings leaves.
Big Graywings leaves.
Each day a flock of gulls
leaves the little island.
Over the tossing waves they fly
leaving the island far behind.

Down below them
porpoises play.
And high above,
the wild geese go flying south.

After two days of flying
and two nights of resting on the waves
Graywings sees a city
on the mainland near the water.
In the harbor of the city
there are freighters, liners, fishing boats.
There are tugboats chugging, chugging.
Ferry boats go back and forth.

Swooping down,
Graywings screams her greeting
from atop a mooring post.

When snow comes
and winter winds blow cold,
there is always food for gulls
in the harbor of the city.
They follow the ships that come and go
and swoop down to snatch
the tidbits thrown overboard.
They gather in great flocks
around the dumps
and gobble up the scraps of food
that come from city kitchens.
Gulls are not the least bit fussy
about their food.

Sometimes
Graywings and a flock of gulls
take long trips to the country.
They soar and circle
above the frozen lakes and rivers,
above the fields and marshes.
Then, on outspread wings,
they coast down to hunt
for seeds and grubs and mice.

And so winter passes.
When spring comes again
Graywings, Big Graywings,
and many other gulls grow restless.
"Klee-eew! Klee-eew! Klee-eew!"
It is time to go back
to the rocky little island
and build another nest.
Many of the young gulls
stay in the harbor of the city
to spend the summer.

But one day
Graywings and Big Graywings
leave the mainland
and fly out across the water
toward the rocky little island
to build another nest
and raise another family.

ABOUT THE AUTHOR

Alice Goudey has written twelve well-known "Here Come" books. She is also the author of several books for a younger age group, among them *Houses from the Sea* and *The Day We Saw the Sun Come Up*, both ALA Notable Books. Her husband, who was Chairman of the Science Department in the Bronxville schools, shares her interest in children and has been of great help with the scientific background of her nature books.

Chauncey D. Leake, President, American Association for the Advancement of Science, has written to Mrs. Goudey: "Your nature study books for children are a splendid contribution to the promotion of a warm and sympathetic interest in natural phenomena."

ABOUT THE ARTIST

Marie Nonnast has illustrated many fine books for children. She was born in Jenkintown, Pennsylvania, and she studied art at the Moore Institute in Philadelphia where she met her husband who is also an illustrator. They now live in New York City with their young son. Mrs. Nonnast is an enthusiastic bird watcher and a butterfly collector.